C000193978

Young Animals

Activity Book

Name: ______________________

Age: ______________________

Class: ______________________

School: ______________________

OXFORD
UNIVERSITY PRESS

Great Clarendon Street, Oxford, OX2 6DP, United Kingdom

Oxford University Press is a department of the University of Oxford.
It furthers the University's objective of excellence in research, scholarship,
and education by publishing worldwide. Oxford is a registered trade
mark of Oxford University Press in the UK and in certain other countries

© Oxford University Press 2013

The moral rights of the author have been asserted

First published in 2013
2020
10 9 8 7 6 5

No unauthorized photocopying

All rights reserved. No part of this publication may be reproduced, stored
in a retrieval system, or transmitted, in any form or by any means, without
the prior permission in writing of Oxford University Press, or as expressly
permitted by law, by licence or under terms agreed with the appropriate
reprographics rights organization. Enquiries concerning reproduction outside
the scope of the above should be sent to the ELT Rights Department, Oxford
University Press, at the address above

You must not circulate this work in any other form and you must impose
this same condition on any acquirer

Links to third party websites are provided by Oxford in good faith and for
information only. Oxford disclaims any responsibility for the materials
contained in any third party website referenced in this work

ISBN: 978 0 19 464654 3

Printed in China

This book is printed on paper from certified and well-managed sources

ACKNOWLEDGEMENTS

Young Animals Activity Book by: Kamini Khanduri

Illustrations by: Kelly Kennedy and Alan Rowe

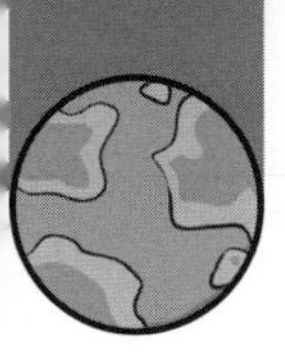

Introduction

1 Find and write the words.

youngnanimalsbabiesadultsfastslowly

1 young 3 ________ 5 ________

2 ________ 4 ________ 6 ________

2 Complete the sentences.

slowly ~~babies~~ animals

1 Young animals grow up from babies into adults.

2 Some young ________ grow up fast.

3 Some young animals grow up ________.

3 Answer the questions. Look at page 3 of *Young Animals*.

1 What are these young animals?

____

2 What young animals do you like?

____

1 Babies

Pages 4–5

1 Write the words.

1 nest

2 l_ _

3 h_ _ _

4 h_ _ _ _

5 b_ _ _

6 e_ _ _

2 Order the words.

1 an egg. / hatch / from / Some babies

Some babies hatch from an egg.

2 a nest. / A mother duck / makes

____

3 its mother. / from / born / is / A baby zebra

____

4 brown and white / has / A baby zebra / stripes.

____

2 Parents

Pages 6–7

1 Complete the puzzle. Then write the secret word.

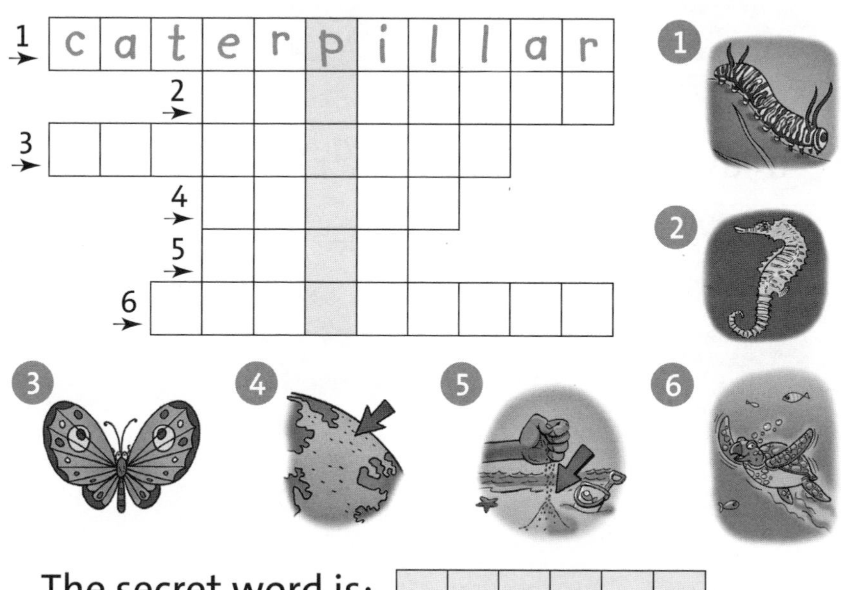

The secret word is: ☐☐☐☐☐☐

2 Circle the correct words.

1 A caterpillar is a butterfly's **parent** / **baby**.

2 Parents protect their **babies** / **mothers**.

3 A mother sea turtle lays her eggs in the **ocean** / **sand**.

4 Baby sea turtles **meet** / **don't meet** their mother.

3 Help Pages 8–9

1 Write the words.

1 tudal

adult

2 ancle

____

3 troptec

____

4 slamina

____

2 Complete the sentences.

mother babies young help

1 Many adult animals __________ young animals.

2 A __________ elephant lives with its mother.

3 A mother chimpanzee carries her __________ .

4 A young ostrich lives with its __________ and father.

4 Danger

Pages 10–11

1 Write the words.

caterpillar shark poison spots
~~kangaroo~~ pouch

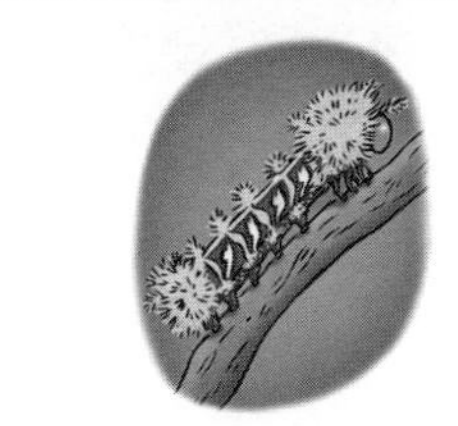

1 Kangaroo 2 ________ 3 ________

4 ________ 5 ________ 6 ________

2 Answer the questions.

1 Where do young kangaroos live?

They live in their mother's pouch.

2 What danger is there for young animals?

____

3 What do some caterpillars have in their body?

____

5 Food

Pages 12–13

1 Find and write the words.

e	d	f	s	e	a	l
b	v	t	o	a	d	f
t	a	d	p	o	l	e
f	g	d	h	o	e	i
w	g	o	w	l	u	h
i	n	s	e	c	t	s

1 toad

2 o

3 s

4 i

5 t

2 Complete the sentences.

milk seal tadpole insects

1 A young ________ drinks its mother's milk.

2 A young owl doesn't drink ________.

3 A toad eats ________.

4 A baby toad is called a ________.

6 Homes

Pages 14–15

Write the words.

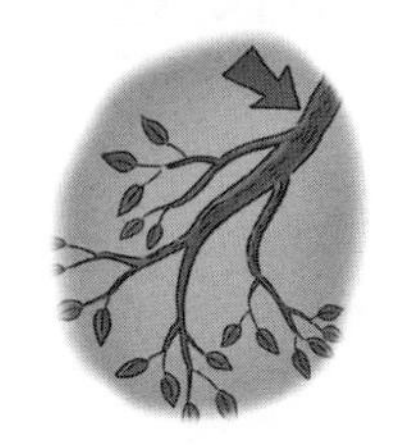

1 b_ _ _   2 m_ _   3 b_ _ _ _ _

4 g_ _ _ _   5 r_ _ _   6 b_ _ _ _ _

Order the words.

1 a home / Bears / make / a den. / called

____

2 are / Young / bears / in the den. / warm

____

3 a lodge. / called / a home / make / Beavers

____

4 A / beaver / young / safe / in the lodge. / is

____

7 How Animals Learn

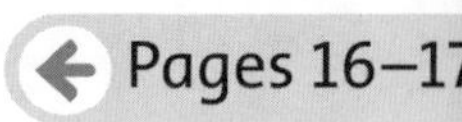

1 Write the words. Then match.

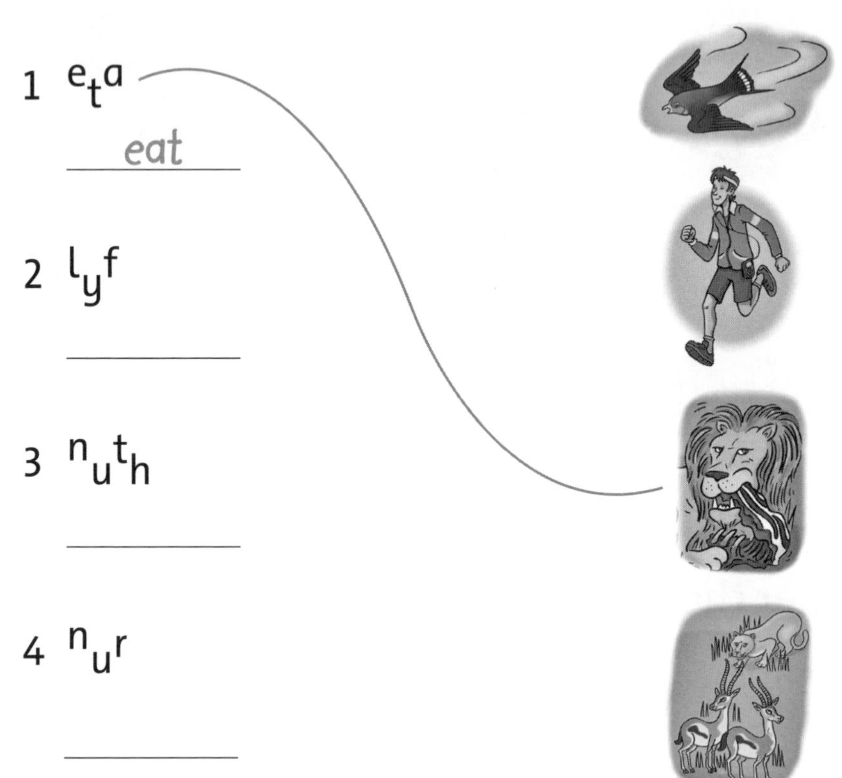

2 Write *true* or *false*.

1 Young animals learn many things. true

2 Young cheetahs learn to fly. ________

3 Young cheetahs learn to hunt. ________

4 An eagle can run more than 100 kilometres per hour. ________

8 How Animals Grow Up

Pages 18–19

1 Write the words.

larva male parents pupa lion beetle

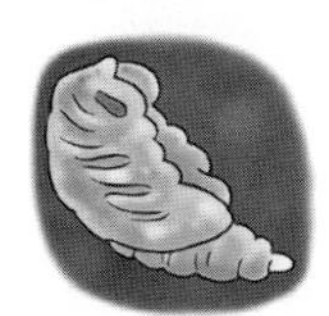

1 ____________

2 ____________

3 ____________

4 ____________

5 ____________

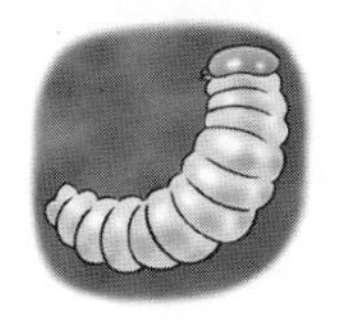

6 ____________

2 Match. Then write the sentences.

Every day,	lives in a pride.
A young lion	young animals are born!
A young beetle	grow up into adults.
Young animals	is called a larva.

1 Every day, young animals are born!

2 ______________________________

3 ______________________________

4 ______________________________

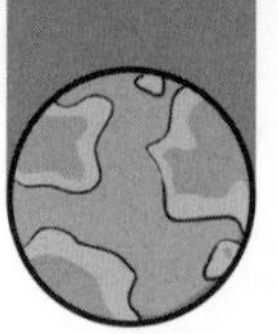

After Reading

Read pages 3–19

1 Complete the Picture Dictionary.

adult

branches

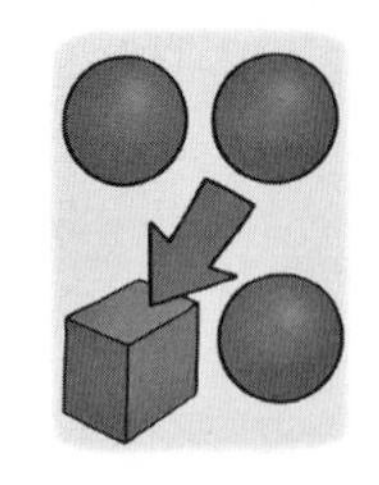

grass

insects

ocean

   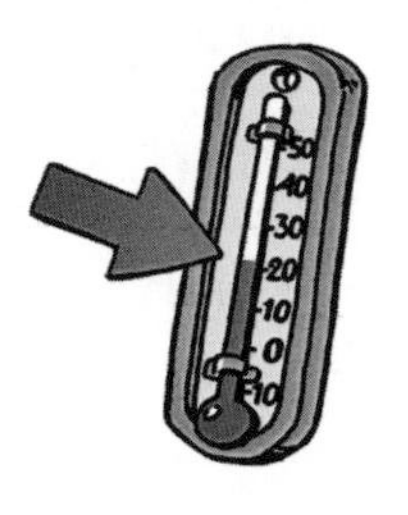

sand

2 Find the words and write the page.

1 Every day, young animals are born! page 19

2 Beavers make a home called a lodge. ________

3 This young shark has spots. ________

4 Some young animals don't meet their parents! ________

5 That's very, very fast! ________

6 A young owl doesn't drink milk. ________

7 They help it to walk, too! ________

8 A baby zebra has brown and white stripes. ________

3 Write about young animals.

Some babies hatch from an ________. Some babies are born from their ________. Many young animals look the same as their ________. There's danger for ________ animals. How do young animals stay ________? Young animals ________ many things. Then they grow up into ________.

4 Complete the chart.

~~ocean~~ ~~mother~~ ~~butterfly~~ born elephant den shark baby bear nest lion toad hatch pouch sea turtle adult lodge kangaroo parent

Animals	butterfly	
Homes	ocean	
Growing Up	mother	

My Book Review

Questions about this book

1 What is this book about?

____

2 Write six new words from this book.

____

____

What I like about this book

My favorite chapter is ______________________.

My favorite picture is ______________________.

My favorite new word is ______________________.

Draw ☺, ☺☺, or ☺☺☺

I like this book. ◯ ◯ ◯

I like the pictures. ◯ ◯ ◯